ISLINGTON

Please return this item on or be̶f̶o̶r̶e̶ ̶t̶h̶e̶ ̶l̶a̶s̶t̶ ̶d̶a̶t̶e̶ ̶s̶t̶a̶m̶p̶e̶d̶ ̶b̶e̶l̶o̶w̶. ...may
be liable to overdue charges. To ... r
access the online catalogue at ... eed
your library membership number

D0715807

101 THINGS

TO DO INSTEAD OF WORRYING ABOUT THE WORLD

FELICITY BRIGHTSIDE

Published in the UK in 2017 by Short Books
Unit 316, ScreenWorks,
22 Highbury Grove, London N5 2ER

10 9 8 7 6 5 4 3 2 1

Copyright © 2017 Short Books

Select illustrations © Shutterstock
Select illustrations © Short Books

A CIP catalogue record for this book is available from the
British Library.

ISBN 978-1-78072-318-1

Printed and bound in Great Britain by
CPI Group (UK) Ltd, Croydon, CR0 4YY

Page Layouts and cover design by Paul Bougourd
Series cover concept created by Two Associates

Introduction

If you're reading this then you've noticed it too. What with climate change, loony world leaders and currency-crushing uncertainty we can't help but feel overwhelmed. Even pets seem more worried than they used to be.

But what if we refused to let it get us down? What if we forgot about the madness and let freedom and positivity reign supreme?

Take a journey through these pages and lose yourself in the simple pleasure of word games, quizzes and mindful exercises. You might just rediscover a calm and tranquility you thought you had forgotten.

1.

Make "Fake News" fun.

Create a front page
full of fake news stories
you'd like to see.

2.

Count your blessings (literally).

Write a list of things that can make you smile, even on a bad day.

1
2
3
4
5
6
7
8

4.

Try this positive wordsearch.

E	A	M	O	D	E	E	R	F
C	T	B	M	S	Y	J	E	C
I	O	R	L	D	L	O	V	E
T	G	H	A	P	P	Y	I	Q
S	E	Y	C	N	E	E	G	U
U	T	Y	E	S	Q	A	F	A
J	H	O	P	E	Y	U	C	L
G	E	L	P	O	E	P	I	E
D	R	E	A	M	E	R	S	L

5.

Look at the full moon through binoculars.

6.

Learn a new skill.

Try construction or bricklaying.
Depending on your political stance,
building walls or building bridges is
the name of the game these days.

Brighten up your route to work by

S C A T T E R I N G

sunflower seeds along the way.

Enjoy watching the flowers grow!

8

Learn to say

"Can we still be friends?"

in the 23 languages of
the European Union.

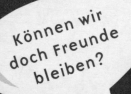

Können wir
doch Freunde
bleiben?

È possibile
rimanere
amici?

9.

Make a wood pile.

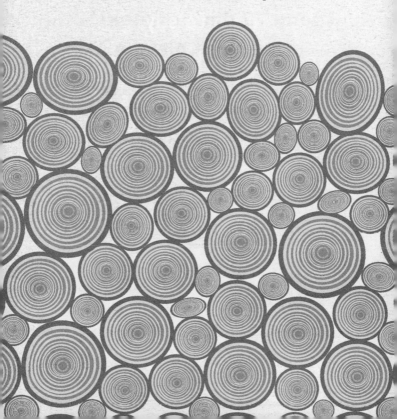

10.

Go to an art gallery and spend 20 minutes looking at just one picture.

11.

Imagine you are the newly-elected Donald Trump.

Which members of your family and friends would you promote to these positions of power?

1. Chief of Staff
(someone who supports you in your role)

2. Press Secretary
(someone who says what you want to say but says it better)

3. Attorney General
(someone who always sticks to the letter of the law)

4. Secretary of the Treasury
(someone who is careful with money)

5. Secretary of Defence
(someone who's good in a fight)

12.

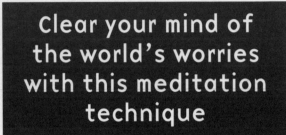

Clear your mind of the world's worries with this meditation technique

1. Sit comfortably somewhere where you won't be disturbed and close your eyes.

2. Breathe naturally.

3. Focus on your breath without trying to alter it. Notice the way breathing in expands your chest, and breathing out contracts it.

4. Don't worry if your mind wanders, just gently bring it back to noticing your breathing.

Try doing this for ten minutes.

13.

See how many words you can make out of these letters.

H	A	U	Q
L	P	I	E
I	Y	P	N
T	S	S	E

(To make a word, each consecutive letter must connect either vertically, horizonally or diagonally.)

14.

Spread a little **happiness** by doing a **good deed** for someone else

Give an unexpected gift, cook a surprise dinner, pay someone else's parking ticket — do one thing today that you know will bring joy.

15.

Get messy and creative with papier mâché.

All you'll need is:

- Newspaper
- Flour
- Water
- Salt
- A balloon
- Paint
- A paintbrush

Make the glue by combining one part flour to one part water until thick and gooey. Add salt. Mix well.

Tear the newspaper into strips and dip them in the glue. Paste onto the balloon and allow it to dry.

Then, simply get painting to make a hot-air balloon, a pig, a face-mask of your celebrity crush... whatever you choose!

16.

Get an insight into the psyche of other cultures...

Match up these untranslatable foreign words with the correct definition opposite:

1. Jayus (Indonesian)

2. Tsundoku (Japanese)

3. Utepils (Norwegian)

4. Lagom (Swedish)

5. Schnapsidee (German)

6. Cafuné (Portuguese)

Definitions:

a) A plan that was formulated when drunk; or one so ridiculous it seems to have been formulated when drunk.

b) A joke that's so unfunny you can't help but laugh.

c) When you buy a book and don't end up reading it (and leave it piled up with other unread books).

d) The act of running your fingers through your lover's hair.

e) To sit outside with a beer on a warm day.

f) Just right; the right amount.

Answers: 1b, 2c, 3e, 4f, 5a, 6d

17.

Play kitchen table tennis.

18.

Write a thank-you letter to someone who's been important to you in your life
(even if you never send it...)

19.

"Every man dies, not every man really lives."
— William Wallace

Don't waste time worrying about the end of the world.

Instead, decide the one thing you've always wanted to do but have been too scared to try.

Set yourself a time limit to make it happen.

What? ....

....

By when? ....

20.

If all else fails, and you can't stop worrying, why not try applying pressure to your "third eye"?

In Chinese medicine it is thought applying pressure to the point directly between your eyebrows can induce a sense of calm and clarity.

21.

Answer these time questions by positioning the hands correctly on the clocks.

1) If the political programme you usually watch starts at 12:20 and lasts for 45 minutes, and you want to avoid it today so as not to be depressed by it all, at what time can you turn the TV back on?

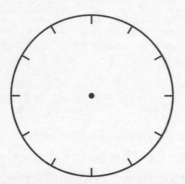

2) If you head out at 12:45 on your bike for a 15-minute cycle to the pub, spend 1 hour 20 minutes there having a relaxing lunch and come straight back, at what time will you arrive home?

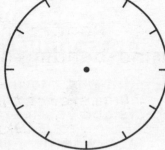

3) If the latest unpleasant celebrity-cum-politician starts a speech at 16:00 and goes on for 1 hour 25 minutes, what time will the nonsense finally be over?

22.

Create your own personalised scent!

Use plant oils known for their calming effects and you'll exude chilled vibes wherever you go.

Plants used in perfumery known to have soothing effects include:

- Bergamot
- Sandalwood
- Mandarin
- Lavender
- Rose
- Lilac
- Ylang-ylang

23.

Organise an office bake-off.

24.

Create a "zen" space in your home.

Pick an
uncluttered area
and use natural
colours, furnishings,
soft lighting and
plants to create
a calm zone.

25

Forget those meditative
colouring books for adults...

Buy a good old-fashioned

**Kid's Colouring
Book.**

Get some crayons and have
Fun going over the lines.

26.

"Say what you see" to work out these visual word puzzles:

1.
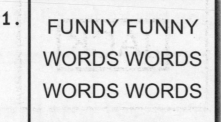

2.
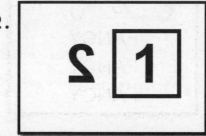

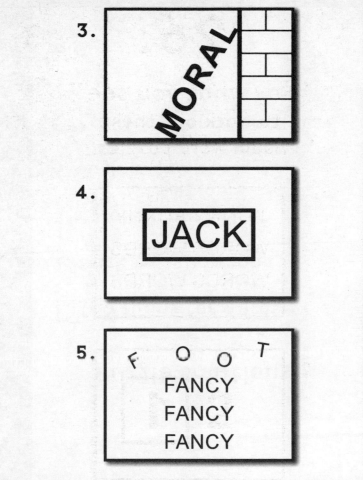

3. MORAL

4. JACK

5. F O O T
FANCY
FANCY
FANCY

Answers over the page

Puzzle Solutions:

1. Too funny for words

2. Back to square one

3. Moral support

4. Jack in the box

5. Footloose and fancy free

27.

Write your own manifesto
for why everybody should
just get along.

28.

Take up a form of martial arts.

Use the guide opposite to find the style that most appeals to you.

Karate
A discipline centred on combat and self-defence originating from the Ryukyu Kingdom.

Tai Chi
A Chinese multi-format discipline used for combat, demonstration or its purported health benefits.

Capoeira
A Brazilian martial art that combines dance and acrobatics.

Krav Maga
An Israeli self-defence discipline derived from street fighting techniques.

Judo
A Japanese educational and combative practice involving throws and takedowns of an opponent.

29.

Take artistic inspiration from the everyday!

Look out of the window and draw, photograph or write a poem about the first thing you see.

Display the fruit of your efforts on the page opposite > > >

Author: _____

Date: _____

30.

Expand your friendship group

by throwing a party and
asking everyone to bring
a friend you haven't
met before.

31.

Learn to appreciate **what you have** with this mindfulness **technique.**

Select five things or people in your daily life that usually pass unnoticed and unappreciated (e.g. the bin men, electricity, a tea bag...)

Think about where they come from, what they do, and what they add to your life.

32.

Take your mind off the state of the nation with this sudoku puzzle:

4	7			8		3		9
		6			9		7	
	3		7			1		5
8		3		1				
	5	7			3	4		2
			2					6
	4			3		6		
	8						5	3
		1		7	2	9		

33.

With Brexit, bail-outs and new trade deals in the offing, why not brush up on your own negotiation skills?

Here are the key steps towards a successful deal:

1. Analyse the problem

2. Work out your goals

3. Listen carefully

4. Speak clearly and concisely

5. Be ready to work with the other side

6. Be friendly and honest to create trust

(the best-laid plans, eh?)

34.

Call your best friend
right now and
**start planning
a road trip.**

How far you go is up to you.

35.

Say what you see
in the inkblot:

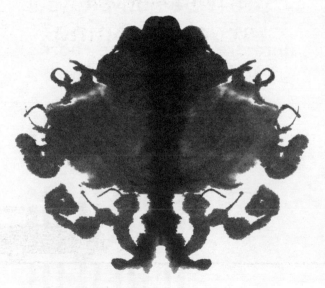

...what does that say about you?

36.

Learn to play
"Let it Be" on piano.

Here are some of the chords
to get you started...

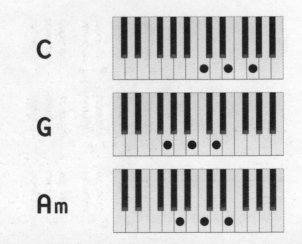

C

G

Am

```
          C                    G
When I find myself in times of trouble,

Am              Fmaj7              F6
Mother Mary comes to me,

C                     G
Speaking words of wisdom,

          F    C
Let it be.
```

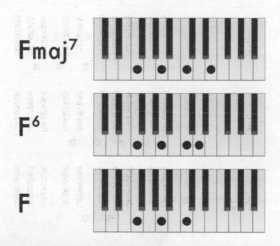

Fmaj7

F6

F

37.

Test your trivia.

See how many of these you can answer without Googling.

1. What was Champagne-maker Dom Pérignon's "day job"?

2. Which planet lies between Saturn and Neptune?

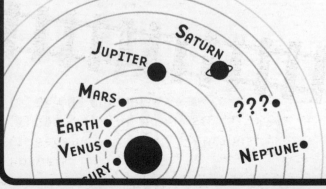

3. In what year were euro coins and notes first used as legal tender?

4. What is the more commonly used name for the painting *La Gioconda*?

5. In what year did the Eurostar train service start?

6. Which comedian starred in the film *The Great Dictator*?

38.

Memorise these responses for when someone tries to engage you in political discussion:

"In the voting booth I just do 'eenie-meenie-miny-mo'."

"I don't know anything about it, but I do love fluffy kittens."

"At times like this I tend to take solace in the wisdom of Winnie the Pooh."

"No hablo inglés."

39.

Create a list of your five
favourite songs with
"happy" in the title.

1

....

2

....

3

....

4

....

5

....

40.

Go for a walk in the rain, splash about in the puddles and get as wet as you can!

41.

Buy a bunch of **flowers** and give them to the first person **you see** who looks like they need **cheering up**

42.

Go for a bike ride.

Why not make it a tandem
ride with a friend?

43.

Become a YouTube sensation!

In principle it's easy; just follow a
cat around with a camera and wait
for it to do something funny.

44

Rediscover the ancient art of Cockney Rhyming Slang.

Try out these phrases:

China plate = mate

Barney Rubble = trouble

Dicky bird = word

Butcher's hook = look

Apples and pears = stairs

Bread and cheese = sneeze

Bubble bath = laugh

e.g. *"C'mon, me ol' china, come up the apples for a quick dicky. We'll have a right bubble, you an' me."*

Try making up your own Rhyming Slang for these words:

Wine

Book

Work

Car

Home

45.

Ponder these mind-bending distances:

Diameter of the earth

12,742km

Diameter of the sun

1,391,400km

Diameter of the Milky Way

9.461×10^{17}km

Distance to the nearest galaxy

2.35×10^{19}km

Reassuring, n'est-ce-pas?
It's all about perspective.

46.

Make puppets out of your odd socks.

47.

Join an open water swimming group.

Crazy in winter, glorious in summer, these groups swim in safe open water all year round — why not don a wetsuit and join them?

48.

Cheer yourself up by writing jokes about world affairs:

"Britain without the EU is like...

....

.... "

"Trump has the classic stylings of...

....

.... "

"On the bright side, nuclear war is...

....

.... "

49.

Go through the contact list on your phone and send a text to someone you haven't spoken to in a while.

CONTACTS
Andy from pub
Angela
Boris
Dave C
Donald
Fitness instructor
Kim (mean one)
Kim (nice one)
Mikey
Mum
Pam from netball

50.

Get positive!

Spend a whole day saying

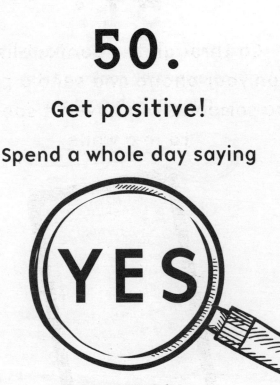

to everything.

51.

Do your bit for international relations by cooking this popular Korean dish:

Ginseng Chicken Soup
or *Samgyetang*

Ingredients:

- 1 medium corn-fed chicken
- 64g short grain, glutinous rice (soak in cold water for 2 hours)

- 2 fresh ginseng roots
- 2 dried jujubes (Korean dates)
- 16 cloves of garlic
- 3 green onions (chopped)
- salt & pepper

Method:

Put the chicken in a large pot. Drain the rice. Stuff the chicken with the ginseng root, jujube, rice and garlic.

Add 2 litres of water to the pan and cook on a high heat for half an hour, then turn down to medium for another 40 minutes or until the chicken is cooked through.

Baste the chicken with the broth from time to time.

Take out the chicken and serve in two bowls with the chopped green onion sprinkled on top.

Serve with traditional Korean dipping sauces.

52.

Kick off your shoes and walk
barefoot on a patch of grass.

(Even if you're not meant to.)

53.

Host a "Hooray for Democracy" party!

Send out invitations in the style of ballot papers, for people to elect their choice of food, drink and entertainment.

54.

Can you match up these words of wisdom with the people who said them?

1. John Lennon

2. Judi Dench

3. Albert Einstein

4. Malala Yousafzai

5. Winston Churchill

6. Emily Dickinson

Answers: 1c, 2f, 3d, 4e, 5b, 6a

a) "Hope is the thing with feathers that perches in the soul."

b) "If you're going through hell, keep going."

c) "Life is what happens to you when you're busy making other plans."

d) "The difference between stupidity and genius is that genius has its limits."

e) "When the whole world is silent, even one voice becomes powerful."

f) "Most things don't work out as expected, but what happens instead often turns out to be the good stuff."

55.

56.

Take a look at this Shakespeare sonnet:

They that have power to hurt and will do none,
That do not do the thing, they most do show,
Who, moving others, are themselves as stone,
Unmovèd, cold, and to temptation slow,
They rightly do inherit heaven's graces,
And husband nature's riches from expense;
They are the lords and owners of their faces,
Others, but stewards of their excellence.
The summer's flower is to the summer sweet,
Though to itself, it only live and die,
But if that flower with base infection meet,
The basest weed outbraves his dignity.
For sweetest things turn sourest by their deeds;
Lilies that fester smell far worse than weeds.

What do you think it says about the deeds of people in power?

57.

Write a pitch for a reality TV show of your life.

Are you more Bear Grylls: the Island, Keeping up with the Kardashians or Gogglebox?

58.

Give your mind a rest from all that bad news.

Create your own 24-hour news blackout.

...and that includes social media!

59.

Take up crocheting.

60.

Help the UK through
the Brexit maze.

61.

Test your lateral thinking.

Connect all of these dots with four straight lines, without taking your pen off the paper or going over any lines twice:

• • •

• • •

• • •

62.

Remember that book everyone raved about that you couldn't finish? Maybe it's time to give it another go...

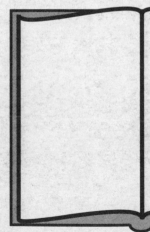

Chapter 1

"Well, Prince, so Genoa and Lucca are now just family estates of the Buonapartes. But I warn you, if you don't tell me that this means war,

63.

Count up the number of nice people you know and the number of mean people you know.

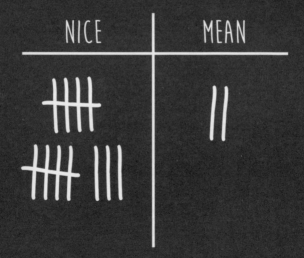

NICE	MEAN
⅂⅂⅂⅂	‖
⅂⅂⅂⅂ ⅂⅂⅂	

See? Things aren't so bad.

64.

Finish the phrase:

"I am awesome
because...

....

....

....
                                            ,,
....

65.

Clean out your cupboards.

Create a word square

where the same four-letter words can be read vertically and horizontally.

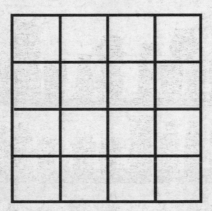

Example:

```
L A T E
A R E A
T E N T
E A T S
```

Brain training!

Find the word that matches both definitions:

1) To be certain of something;
   good or beneficial effect

2) A 360° rotation;
   overthrow of social order

3) To posit a theory;
   to invest capital

4) Being in agreement;
   simultaneous musical notes

5) Shines brightly;
   not heavy

68.

Buy a treat
just for you.

It doesn't matter what it is,
just as long as it makes you smile.

69.

Write a list of five good things in the world that won't change during this time of political upheaval.

1

2

3

4

5

70.

Practise calligraphy.

Happiness

71.

Have a bar of chocolate.

Go on, enjoy it!
(Just make sure it's Fair Trade)

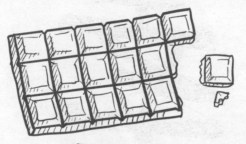

72.

Stay up all night
with friends and
watch the sunrise

73.

Draw a picture of the desert island you would like to escape to when it all gets too much:

74.

Can you solve these riddles?

1. No one wants one, but if you have one you definitely don't want to lose it. What is it?

2. I am found in the sea and on land but I do not walk or swim. I travel by foot but I am toeless. No matter where I go, I'm never far from home. What am I?

3. A girl was ten on her last birthday and will be twelve on her next birthday. How is this possible?

75.

Learn to do a kickturn on a skateboard

(where you lift your front wheels off the
ground and rotate on the back wheels.)

76.

Alphabetise your book, film or music collection.

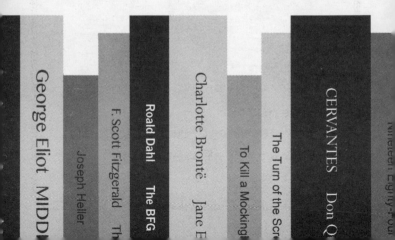

77.

Forget political forecasts and exit polls — work out what's coming next by reading Tarot cards.

Here are a few to look out for:

The Sun:
Material happiness, contentment

Strength:
Power, courage, magnanimity

The Wheel of Fortune:
Destiny, fortune, success

78

Turn off the tap when
you brush your teeth.

79.

Colour in this bird.

Zen Buddhists believe concentrating
on repetitive patterns and
actions stills your mind.

80.

Which of these bizarre statements were made by a US President?

"The beauty of me is that I'm very rich."

"It's freezing and snowing in New York — we need global warming!"

"My IQ is one of the highest — and you all know it! Please don't feel so stupid or insecure; it's not your fault."

"You know, it doesn't really matter what [the media] write as long as you've got a young and beautiful piece of ass."

(*psst!* All of them were said by one US President. No points for guessing who...)

81.

Solve this anagram to find the mathematically correct answer to the sum:

eleven plus two

82.

Rid your mind of worrying thoughts with this visualisation technique.

Create a visual image of what's worrying you, then imagine blowing a huge bubble around it. Now simply blow the bubble away and watch it drift off into the distance.

83. Climb a tree.

84.

Take a day trip to somewhere you've never been before.

Head to the station and don't decide where you're going until you reach the ticket office.

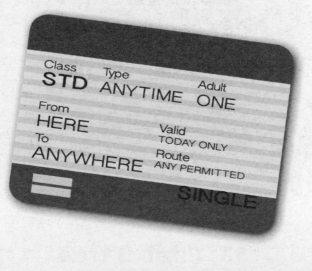

Class STD Type ANYTIME Adult ONE

From HERE

Valid TODAY ONLY

To ANYWHERE

Route ANY PERMITTED

SINGLE

85.

Brush up on your
dystopian novels
to remind yourself that,
no matter how bad
things may seem,
they could always
be much worse!

Here are four classics
to get you started:

Brave New World by Aldous Huxley

Nineteen Eighty-Four by George Orwell

The Handmaid's Tale by Margaret Atwood

Do Androids Dream of Electric Sheep? by Philip K. Dick

86

Have a
water fight.

87.

Ration your screen time.

No more Instagram on the loo or iPad surfing before bed; get your eyes off your screen and your head back in the clouds!

88.

Write down your deepest secret.

...Now show it to someone you trust.

89.

Make a "good news" scrapbook.

PET DOG RETURNS TO FAMILY AFTER [...] YEAR ABSENCE

UNIFIED PLAN ANNOUNCED TO SOLVE GLOBAL WARMING

FOOTBALLER DONATES YEAR'S WAGES TO CHARITY

RED WINE GOOD FOR YOU SAY EXPERTS

[P]OLITICIAN WHO IS INCAPABLE OF LYING

WORLD PEACE DECLARED

CAT RESCUED FROM TREE BY HUMAN PYRAMID

FROG FOUND THAT CAN RIBBIT 'QUE SERA SERA'

101 WAYS TO CHANGE THE WORLD FROM YOUR BED

NO NEWS AT ALL TODAY

MARATHON RUNNER RESCUES CHILD FROM BURNING HOUSE

Ignore the doom and gloom of the headlines; instead make it your mission to find at least one piece of good news a day.

90.

Go for a picnic.

Take some of these calming foods with you to make it the ultimate relaxing al fresco dining experience...

- Blueberries

    (a great source of vitamins C and K, and rich in antioxidants)

- Crab meat

    (good for memory and cognitive function)

- Hardboiled eggs

    (a source of zinc, iron and B vitamins; good for mental clarity)

- Quinoa

    (the king of slow-release energy)

- Baby tomatoes

    (these contain serotonin - also known as the "happiness hormone")

91.

Help reduce someone else's stress and worry with this little stratagem.

Next time you see someone reading a newspaper on the train, put your hand reassuringly on their shoulder and say:

I can't tell you how I know, but it's all going to be okay.

...then just smile cryptically and walk away.

92.

<u>To Hope</u>

by John Keats

When by my solitary hearth I sit,

And hateful thoughts enwrap my soul in gloom;

When no fair dreams before my "mind's eye" flit,

And the bare heath of life presents no bloom;

Sweet Hope, ethereal balm upon me shed,

And wave thy silver pinions o'er my head!

Follow in the footsteps of Keats and write your own poem about hope:

My poem

....

....

....

....

....

....

....

Author: _____

Date: _____

93.

"Lets face it; if its change youre after then youll find most people wont be on your side. But, if its right, theyll get it eventually – yesterdays gone and tomorrows a new day."

94.

Host a "one world" dinner party

where everyone brings a different national dish.

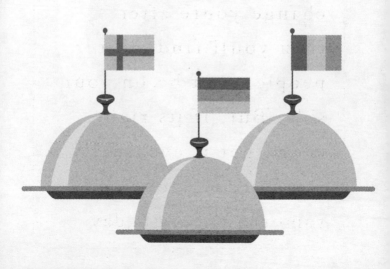

95.

Take up archery.

(If we really are headed for
Armageddon, we'd all be
less worried if we were able to
hunt and gather our own food.)

96.

Clean the
skirting boards.

97.

Complete the proverbs.

Each letter has a corresponding number.
Use the first phrase below as a key,
but you'll also need some guesswork!

E	V	E	R	Y		C	L	O	U	D		H	A	S
13	16	13	22	26		4	2	19	10	20		7	17	5

A		S	I	L	V	E	R		L	I	N	I	N	G
17		5	3	2	16	13	22		2	3	24	3	24	6

—	—	—	—	—	—		—	—	—
7	19	22	5	13	5		14	19	22

—	—	—	—	—	—	—
4	19	10	22	5	13	5

___ ___   ___ ___ ___ ___   ___ ___
24 19   24 13 1 5   3 5

___ ___ ___ ___   ___ ___ ___ ___
6 19 19 20   24 13 1 5

___ ___ ___ ___ ___   ___ ___ ___ ___ ___ ___ ___
21 10 3 2 20   21 22 3 20 6 13 5

___ ___ ___   ___ ___ ___ ___ ___
24 19 25   1 17 2 2 5

___ ___ ___   ___ ___ ___ ___ ___ ___ ___
25 7 13   20 17 22 11 13 5 25

___ ___ ___ ___   ___ ___   ___ ___ ___ ___
7 19 10 22   3 5   9 10 5 25

___ ___ ___ ___ ___ ___   ___ ___ ___ ___
21 13 14 19 22 13   20 17 1 24

Answers over the page

Proverb Answers:

1. Horses for courses

2. No news is good news

3. Build bridges not walls

4. The darkest hour is just before dawn

98.

Design your own flag
for a single world nation
without borders.

Everybody needs to
have a dream.

Write yours down

(seeing it in black and white might just
give you the push to make it a reality.)

100.

Have a nice cup of tea
and a sit down.

101.

Now that you're no longer
worrying about the world,
go and fly a kite.